UCTION
DOWN

SCHOLASTIC INC.
New York Toronto London Auckland
Sydney Mexico City New Delhi Hong Kong

CONSTR
COUNT

by **K. C. Olson**

Illustrated by **David Gordon**

CONSTRUCTION
COUNTDOWN

Ten mighty dump trucks
rolling down the road

Nine earthmovers

9

scraping up a load

Eight bulldozers
reshaping the ground

Seven
payloaders

7

moving
dirt around

6

Six grumbling graders
leveling the land

Five heavy rollers packing down the sand

4

Four concrete mixers
turning while they travel

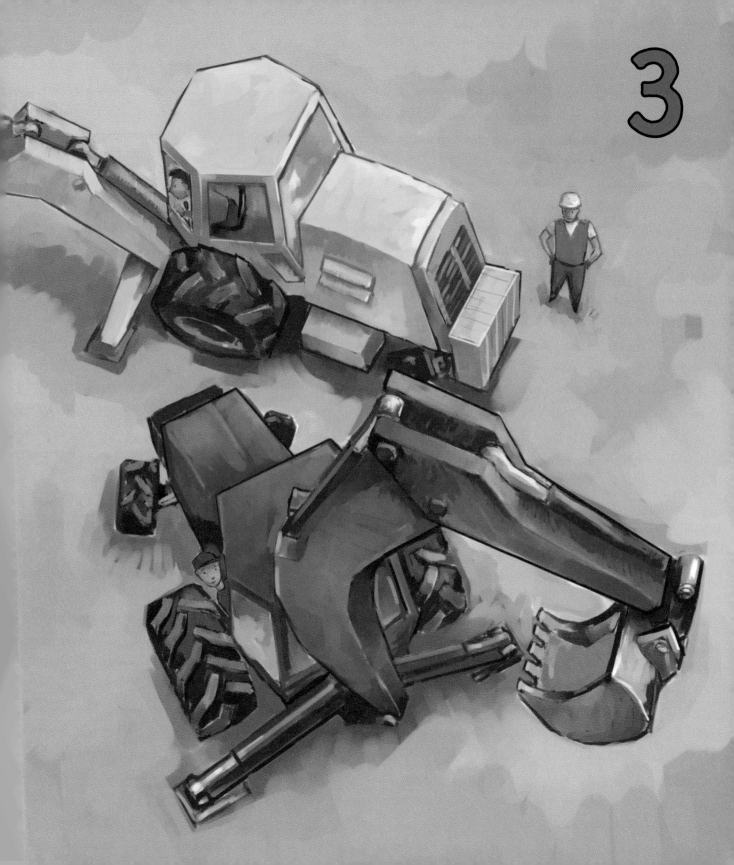

3

2

Two skid loaders,
with lots of loads to haul

And one
gigantic sandbox

with room
to drive them all!

For Kirby and Aren, for starting the engine
—K. C. O.

For my dearest Susan
—D. G.

ISBN 978-0-545-32832-6

Text copyright © 2004 by K. C. Olson. Illustrations copyright © 2004 by David Gordon. All rights reserved. Published by Scholastic Inc., 557 Broadway, New York, NY 10012, by arrangement with Henry Holt and Company, LLC. SCHOLASTIC and associated logos are trademarks and/or registered trademarks of Scholastic Inc.

12 11 10 9 8 7 6 5 4 3 2 1   10 11 12 13 14 15/0

Printed in the U.S.A.   08

First Scholastic printing, December 2010

Book designed by Martha Rago and Patrick Collins

The artist used Painter 6.0 and Adobe Photoshop on a Macintosh computer to create the illustrations for this book.